Spirit

Courage

Hope

Inspiration

Love

Family

Family

Inspiration

Attitude

Spirit

Courage

Courage

Hope

Attitude

Patience

Attitude

Spirit

Family

Inspiration

Courage

Hope

Spirit

Love

Attitude

Hope

Family

Inspiration

Spirit

Hope

Family

Inspiration

Patience

Inspiration

Razz

Merlin

Whimze

The Tail of Razz's Journey

by **Razz,** as told through
Donna Doyle, animal communicator,
with Merlin, Whimze, Claudia and Bruce Winkle

Illustrated by
Penny Hauffe

Remember
Time heals almost everything.
So give the time, some time.

Zentangle Corgi Clock by Kathleen Stemler
www.KathleensArtCreations.com

Printed in USA   Published by: Merrazz-LLC   First Edition 2018

US $16.95   ISBN # 978-0-9846868-4-1   All rights reserved

The photos in this book were kindly taken and shared by the members of Team Razz using their cell phones.

This is the inspirational journey
of Razz recovering from disc surgery
with the support of his family
and friends.

My first day home.

I wanted my story to be told
to encourage others to face their
challenges and life lessons.

Emergency vet.

One day I woke up and I couldn't walk very well. Something was wrong with my rear legs. They were wobbly.

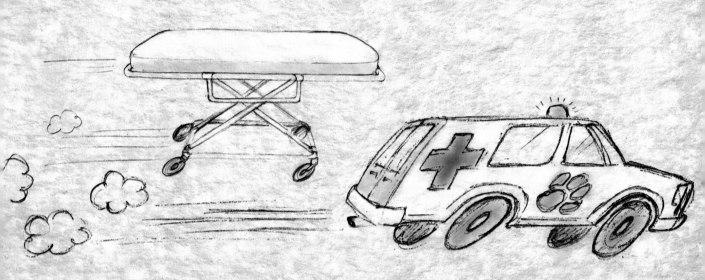

So Mom and Dad
rushed me over to the
emergency vet.

I needed an MRI
to see what was happening
to me.

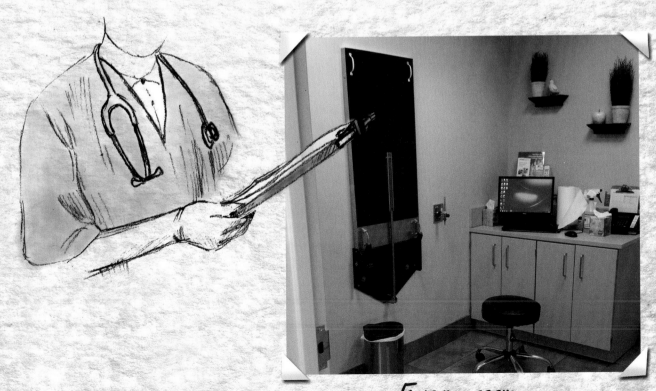

Exam room.

An MRI is a safe and painless test that uses magnetic fields and radio waves to show detailed pictures of the body.

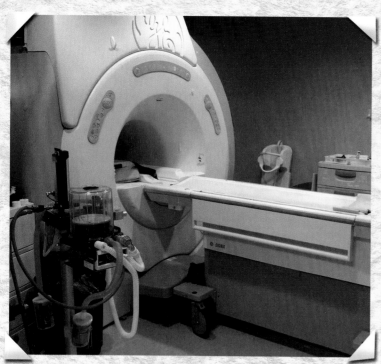

MRI Machine.

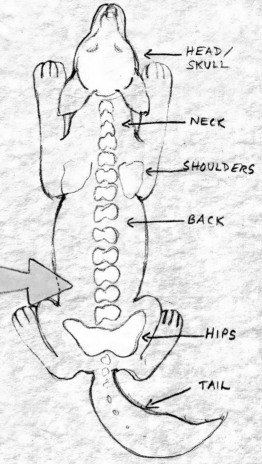

HEAD/SKULL

NECK

SHOULDERS

BACK

REPAIRS NEEDED

HIPS

TAIL

The MRI scans showed I had ruptured discs in my lower back.

After Mom and Dad talked to the vets,
it was decided surgery was the best solution.

Mom told me to "be brave" but
I was really scared.

Through this journey I have learned
that it's okay to be afraid,
and scared of the uncertain.

Remember
your family
is there
to help you
when you
are feeling
fearful and
not so sure
of yourself.

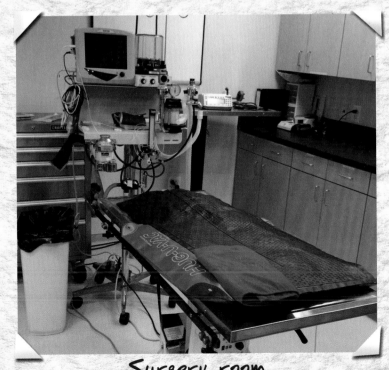

Surgery room.

Hospital room.

After my surgery,
I stayed here for
six days and six nights.
In dog speak, that is
6 suns and 6 moons.

It took a lot of courage to be here
without my Mom, my Dad and my brothers.

To help me heal faster
I received hyperbaric oxygen
treatments.

Oxygen therapy tank.

Hyperbaric oxygen therapy involves
exposing the body to high pressure oxygen
to speed up the healing process.

"Until one has loved an animal,
a part of one's soul remains unawakened."

My friends at
the surgery center.

All the nurses and vets took really good care of me. They gave me medication for my pain.

We became friends and they helped me not to be so afraid.

They called me "Razzle dazzle", "Razzie", "Razzle-Licious" and "Razzamatazzie".

I became one of their star patients, and now my photo greets others when they come to the surgery center.

Star Patient

My portrait.

Settling into my space.

I finally was able to come home!

I received many get-well cards
from friends and family.

I have to say I love that
Mom and Dad are always
here for me.

Home in time for Christmas.

Electrostim acupuncture.

This may look really scary to you.

Yet, as you look at my picture you can see I am really relaxed.

Acupuncture improves how the body works and helps decrease pain while helping with healing.

While Dad meditates with me
I get a warm feeling.

When I bring all my energy here
to this present moment, I am able to
open my heart to the peaceful power
of my Dad's energy
and
the healing of acupuncture.

Meditation with Dad.

My space is nice and neat.

I like to rearrange my pen
just to keep myself busy.

I cuddle up with my toy friends
and move them around until
we are all comfortable.

Sometimes I just pile them up.
I love to do this when no one is looking.

Now my space is just right.

Massage is my most favorite treatment.

Oooh!

I would love to receive massage all day long.

Massage from Michelle.

I wonder if Michelle could move in?

It feels good
to be rubbed all over.

The smell of lavender
and
almond oil
helps me relax.

Heat therapy.

Exercise ball.

The exercise ball supports
building my core muscles and stamina.
At first, I was afraid I was going to
fall off the exercise ball.

It took me some time to get used to
this therapy. Finally, I realized
that it was helping me.

After all, I love to play ball.
Oh, did I tell you, I love to play ball?

Honestly, I don't feel anything
with the laser therapy.
It doesn't hurt.
It helps relax my muscles
and heals scar tissue.

Laser therapy.

Laser therapy lessens pain, reduces swelling

and helps repair nerves.

This looks like a big fish tank to me.

Treadmill water therapy.

I want to thank all my friends at the rehab center.

The first time they
put these goggles
on me I thought
  I was going deep
          sea diving or flying in a plane.

I quickly learned that I was not swimming
or doing the dog paddle. I was walking
    on the treadmill under the water.

    The water
    helps support
    me, so I can
    walk on my own.

SPEEDOG

Cool goggles.

CERTIFICATE OF COMPLETION

VSCR
Rehabilitation at
Veterinary Surgical Centers

This is to certify that

RAZZ WINKLE

is a **SWIMMING EXPERT** at Veterinary Surgical Centers Rehabilitation

April 26, 2018
Date

Congratulations from the entire VSCR team!

Treadmill time on my own.

TOWEL

Towel time.

Sometimes I get a weird tingly feeling
in my back legs while I
am on the treadmill.

I love the water.
It is my second
favorite thing
to do.

at @ The
LIFE CENTRE
WEST

Don't feel sorry for me.

My harness.

Before my wheels
we used a harness
to help get me
get around.

Now I have wheels! Brand new wheels.
What the heck am I going to do?
I love the freedom.

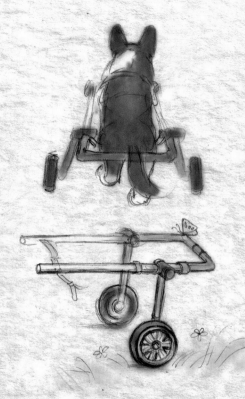

New wheels.

I feel I can do anything my brothers can do.
"Wheee!"
I am flying on my wheels. I can even pop
a wheelie. Nothing can hold me back now.
I am even studying for my driver's license!

The first time I used my wheels many
of the neighbors came out and cheered
me on as I walked down the block.

My Mom started to cry, and I was just
so excited to
be out in the
neighborhood
again.

Licensed to drive.

Leg lifts.

Leg lifts help me strengthen my balance.

Here I am doing theraband therapy.
Just so you know, this is not
my favorite exercise.

This is a lesson about doing what
is good for you even if you don't like it.
Still, that won't change my mind
about the theraband therapy.

Theraband therapy.

Playing in my pool.

Yay!

Yay!

Yay!

Kick Board

Team Razz swim cap

Noodle

TEAM RAZZ

SWIM

TRUNKS

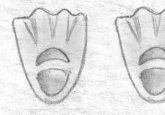

I also love being
in the pool
on our deck.

This is playtime
for me,
not therapy.

SWIM
TRAINING

2 x Freestyle
2 x Backstroke
2 x Butterfly
2 x Breaststroke
2 x Doggie
Paddle

Home swimming.

Training for rally.

I really like to train for rally.
I earned my advanced title before my
surgery and only needed one more qualifying
event to receive my excellent title.

I really believe that
handicapped/disabled/physically
challenged dogs and people
should be included in
more events around
the world.

Having fun!

Did you know that the tail connects with the root chakra for a dog? The root chakra is about being safe and secure in your body.

Wagging my tail.

Can you see my tail wagging? This means I am happy. So mainly I just keep wagging my tail.

My hope is to someday fully recover and get out of my wheels.

If not, I am loved and that is what is most important. At times, I have been worried that I might disappoint my Mom, Dad or my brothers.

Because my right leg drags sometimes we put a balloon bootie on it.

Have you ever put a balloon on your foot? Please, don't try this by yourself.

I have blue, purple and neon green booties.

Wagging with my wheels.

Rainbow Razz.

Did you know
that rainbows symbolize
hope, harmony and connection?
If you connect your heart in rainbow light
you know that there is no situation that
cannot be healed and that there is always
hope.

Because I am so special a rainbow can be seen.

Holy Guacamole!

I wrap myself up like a burrito.
But only when Mom and Dad
are not watching.

Burrito Razz.

Good citizen award.

THE AMERICAN KENNEL CLUB

Canine Good Citizen Title Certificate

This certifies that

DOBCARR'S RAZZAMATAZZ RA CGC ~ DN29325501

Owned by

CLAUDIA & BRUCE WINKLE

successfully passed the Canine Good Citizens Test on

FEBRUARY 15, 2017

and has been officially recorded as a Canine Good Citizen
by the American Kennel Club

Mary R. Burch
Canine Good Citizen Director

RAZZ

AKC Good Citizen test

1. Accepting a friendly stranger.
2. Sitting politely for petting.
3. Appearance and grooming.
4. Walking on a loose leash.
5. Walking through a crowd.
6. Sit and down on command
   and staying in place.
7. Coming when called.
8. Reaction to another dog.
9. Reacting or not reacting
   to a distraction.
10. Supervised separation.

My brothers and I earned the
"Canine Good Citizen" award together.
Really, it was nothing.
It was easy, since we are all pretty smart.
I helped my brothers get through their test.

Celebrating with my brothers.

Merlin

I want to say that all Razz has gone through has affected me personally. I was worried about Razz. I didn't know where he went for 6 suns and 6 moons.

I wish Mom and Dad would have told me what was going on. When Razz finally came home I felt separated from him. I didn't know how to help. All I knew was Razz was getting all the attention. I felt left out. I didn't know what to do.

I wanted to be supportive, yet I felt bad for Razz and wished that Whimze and I could have done something to help our brother. As I watched, I began to understand better what was happening with him.

All we wanted to do was play together again like we used to do.

I felt guilty because I was healthy, and Razz was not. This has hurt my heart and made me sad to watch.

Razz and I have always had a very close connection. I know that Razz loves us. I now realize I should just trust that everything will be okay.

Remember to love your siblings no matter what happens.

Time together on the patio.

Whimze

I have been affected emotionally and I feel guilty and wish that this happened to me instead of Razz.

I didn't always know what Razz was doing and why Razz was getting all the attention. I felt a little jealous and guilty at the same time.

I now understand that Razz is okay and would like to get better and be able to walk on his own. I would add that all the siblings need to be included in what is going on with the family.

I also would like to do more and be more involved to help Razz.
I was thinking I could go to swim therapy with Razz to show my support for him.
After all I would love an extra ride in the car.

Razz is my "brudder" and I love him, and it is hard to see Razz not doing all the things Merlin and I are doing. As time has gone by Razz and I are now able to play together.

Razz may not be able to do all the things he used to do, but we still find ways to have fun.

Playing with my "brudder".

Razz

My name is Razzamatazz and I wanted to share my story of healing. Hopefully, my journey will encourage you to be brave.

Here are some of the lessons I have learned and have taught to others:

* Don't ever give up.
* Be patient with yourself and others.
* Don't feel sorry for yourself.
* Always have a positive attitude.
* Things may not always go your way but that's okay. Sometimes they end up even better.

* Take one day at a time.
* Always try to do your best.
* Don't push yourself too hard (especially if it is hot and humid).
* The hard times we experience always light up the lessons we need the most.

What a journey it has been.
I know that I could not have made it through without my family and friends.
It takes a team to take care of me.
I know there are so many that love me, and I want them to know that I love them.

I am really proud of my Mom and Dad for writing this book with me.

Standing on my own.

Mom

As parents there were a lot of unknowns since there has been no handbook for this journey.

We have also learned many lessons.

The biggest lesson is about trying to enjoy the journey of healing and not just getting to the destination of Razz walking on his own again.

We should have communicated early on to Merlin and Whimze to let them know what was happening with Razz.
Razz has a very special gift of not giving up and sometimes has pushed himself too hard. This has resulted in numerous setbacks.

He has been a source of hope and inspiration to all of us.
As Razz would say "Always make the best of every situation".

Watching Razz fly out of the garage door, on his back side, puts a whole new meaning to "hauling ass".

This reminds us of a quote by Martin Luther King, Jr.
> *"If you can't fly, run.*
> *If you can't run, walk.*
> *If you can't walk, crawl.*
> *But by all means, keep moving."*

Where Razz's journey will take him we really don't know. We know that it is his goal to walk again and we will continue to support him on his path. Razz has told us that he is really glad that we are telling his story.

Dad

Thank you to Team Razz

Wholistic Paws Veterinary – www.wholisticpawsvet.com
Krisi Erwin -DVM, CVA, CCRT   **and**   **Kasey Braun** – LVT, CMT
Acupuncture, Laser Therapy, Herbal Supplements, Massage.

Michelle Jackson – Dog Trainer
Thera-bands, balance ball, home swimming, massage,
wheel therapy, rally training.

Angela Snook – Angel "A" Dog Walker
Play therapy, wheel therapy, massage.

Pedro Reyes – Uncle Pedro
Massage, wheel therapy, swimming.

A special thank you to all of Razz's supporters and friends at:

Bush Veterinary Neurology Services - www.bvns.net
MRI, surgery, in hospital care, hyperbaric oxygen treatments.

Veterinary Surgical Centers and Rehabilitation - www.vscvets.com
Under water treadmill and laser therapy.

Walkin Wheels - www.handicappedpets.com
For their wonderful wheels.

Petplan - www.gopetplan.com. On this journey we have been fortunate to have pet insurance. It has helped tremendously to offset some of the cost of the surgery and therapies.

Even if you do not have insurance, you can learn to do many of these therapies for your pet.

Books by Merlin, Razz and Whimze:

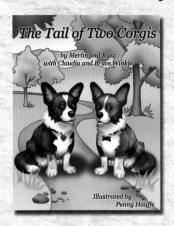  

Our books are available on our website,
www.merrazz-llc.com

Penny is a world traveled and celebrated painter and sculptor living and working in Leesburg, Virginia. Her commissioned work has appeared nationally and as far away as Australia, South Africa and the UK. She creates artwork for many shows throughout much of Loudoun County, Va. Penny is also the illustrator for the "Corgis" other three books.

Penny Hauffe – www.pennypaint.com

Donna has been doing Animal Communication Consultations and Workshops since the loss of her beloved dog Keisha in 2003 and has been practicing Reiki for Animals since 2004. She has helped various organizations raise money by doing readings at their fundraising events and helped many rescues by speaking to the animals to help them get adopted.

Donna Doyle – www.donnadoolittle.com

♥ A special thank you to Peny Gallogy for her assistance in reviewing this book.

♥ A special thank you to Angela Bell for her assistance with our website.